# BUG-EYED

## PUZZLES TO TURN YOUR EYEBALLS INSIDE OUT

Flying Frog Publishing

Copyright © 2001 Flying Frog Publishing
Imprint of Allied Publishing Group, Inc.

P9-DHI-013

# The ANTS go marching . . .

Find the three (3) ants that do NOT have six (6) legs!!!

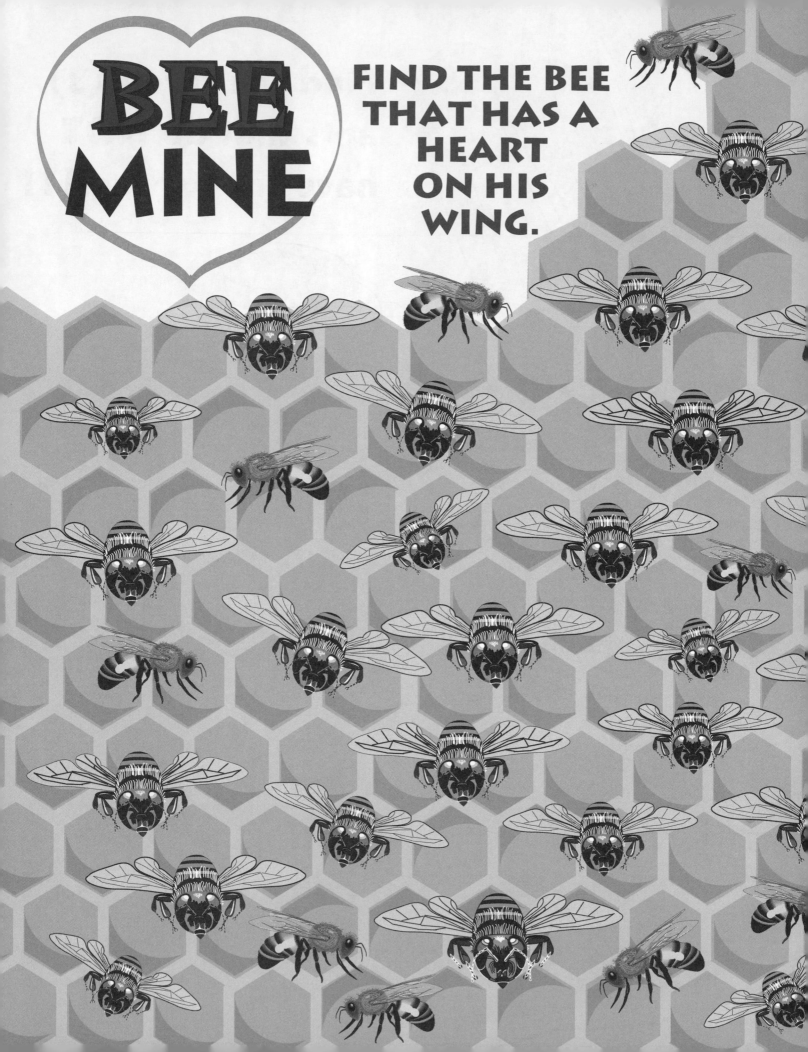

# BUTTERFLY BONANZA

*Which butterfly has the most friends with the same pattern? You will be surprised!!!*

# CENTIPEDE CENTRAL

**Find the other centipedes that also have 42 legs**

*HINT: there are 5

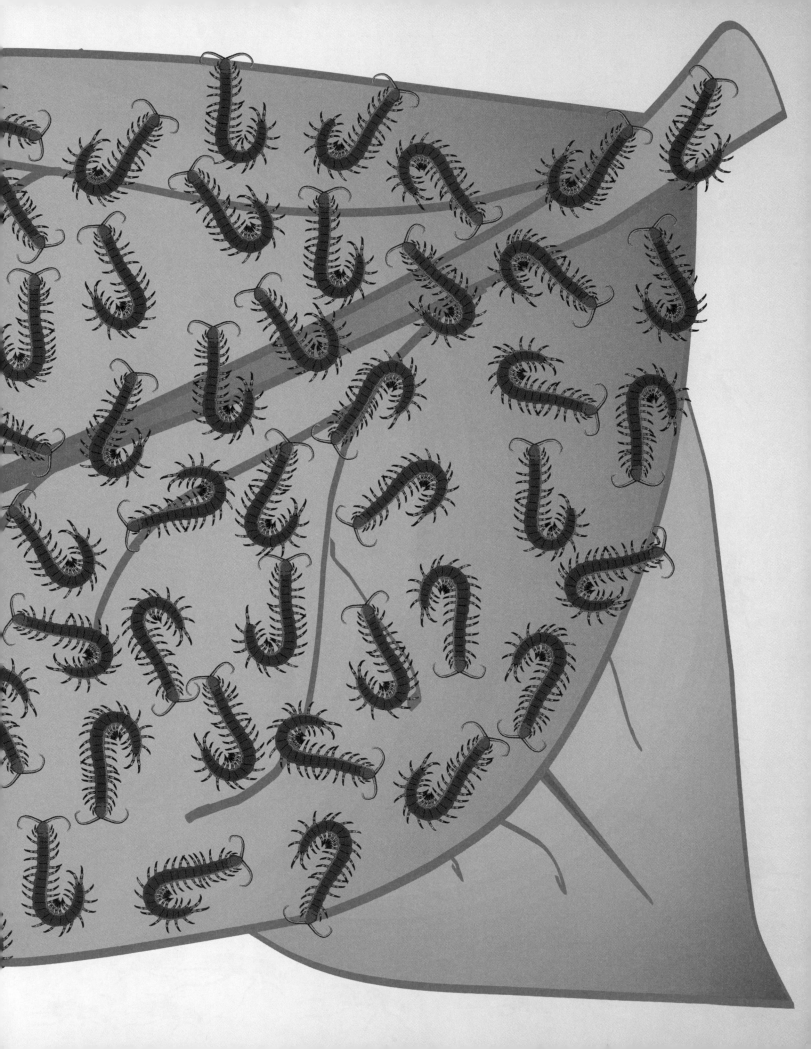

# Time to Get the Bug Spray!!!

Find the one cockroach that is different.

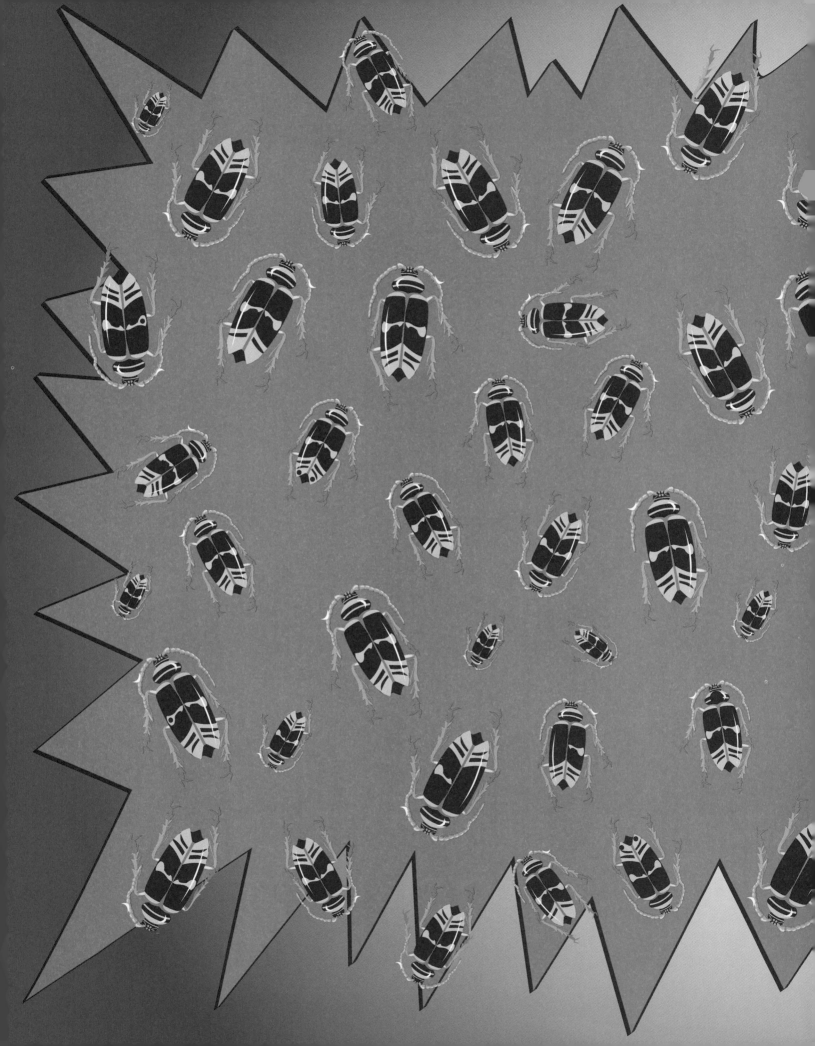

# BUG·A·BOO

Find my three (3) obnoxious brothers who look just like me, they may or may not be the same size, but the pattern is the same.

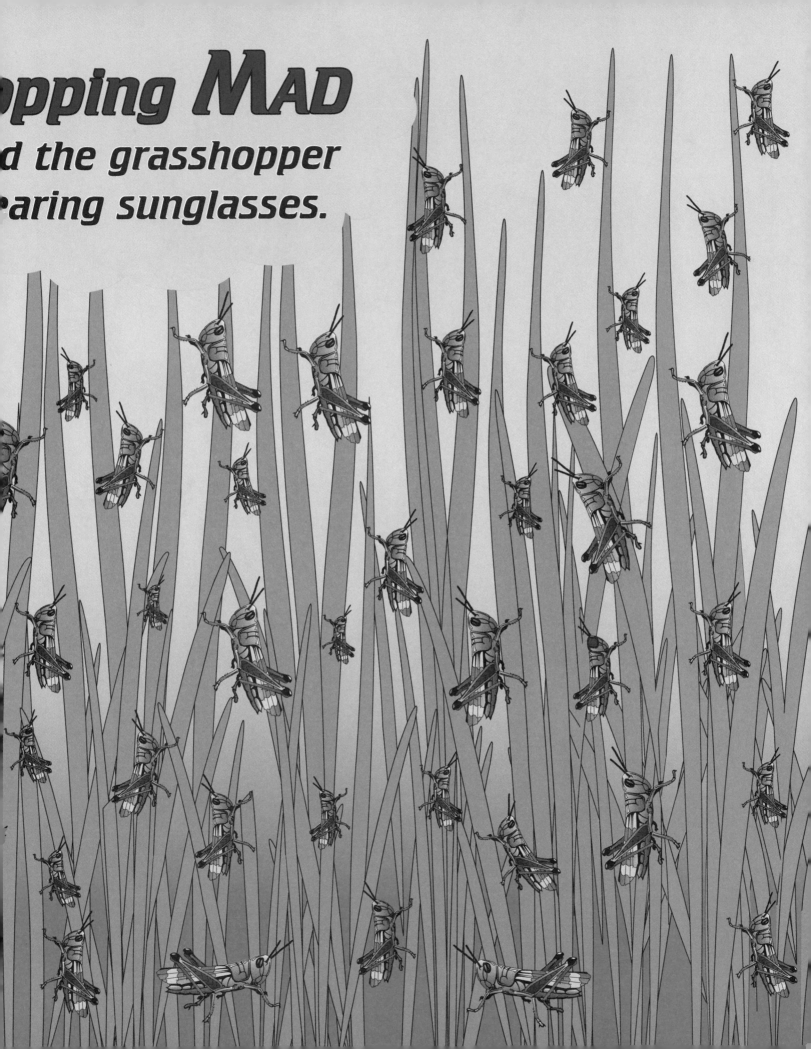

# pping MAD

## d the grasshopper ring sunglasses.

# FIVE ALIVE!!!
Find the 5 harlequin beetles that are exactly alike. (No More, No Less)

# Lady Luck!!

Momma ladybug
has quintuplets,
help her round them up,
they look exactly like her.

# Mantis Munch

**Find the hidden let**
**on the Praying Mar**
**one has a P**
**another has a M.**

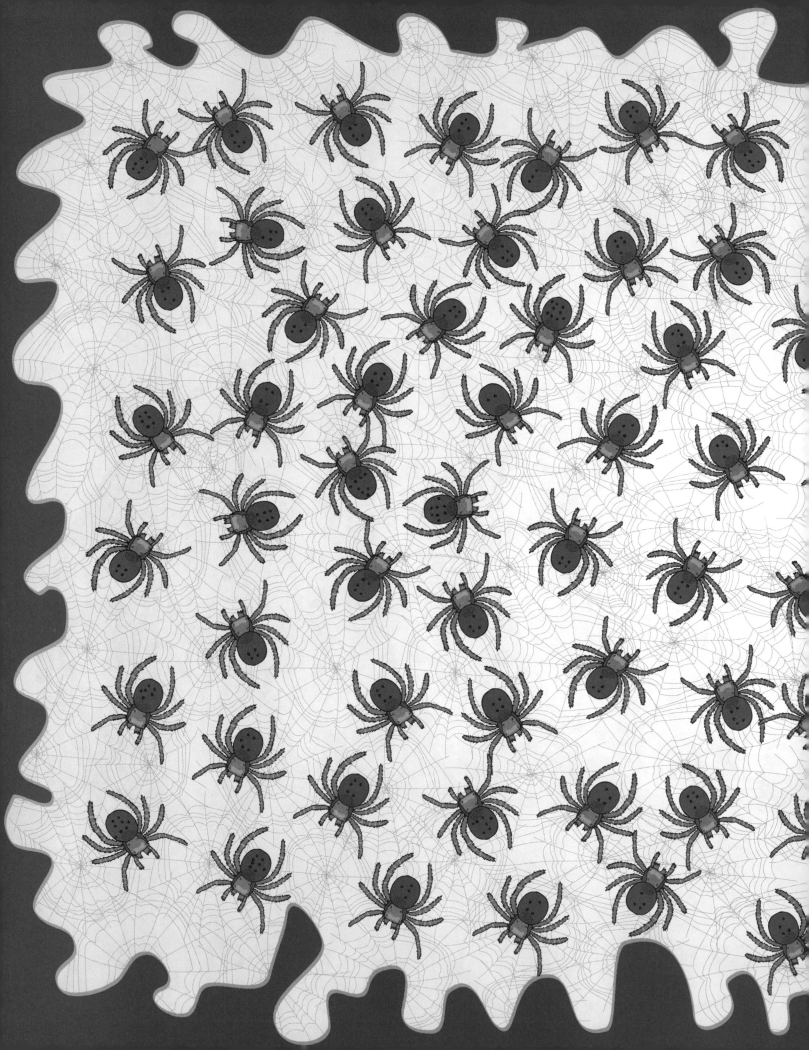

# SPIDER SPASM

Look at me and find 3 more exactly like me!

# Sticks and Stones may. . .

**You have 30 seconds - time it!-**
**to count the stick bugs.**
•**HINT it's one of these**•
**100 • 95 • 110**

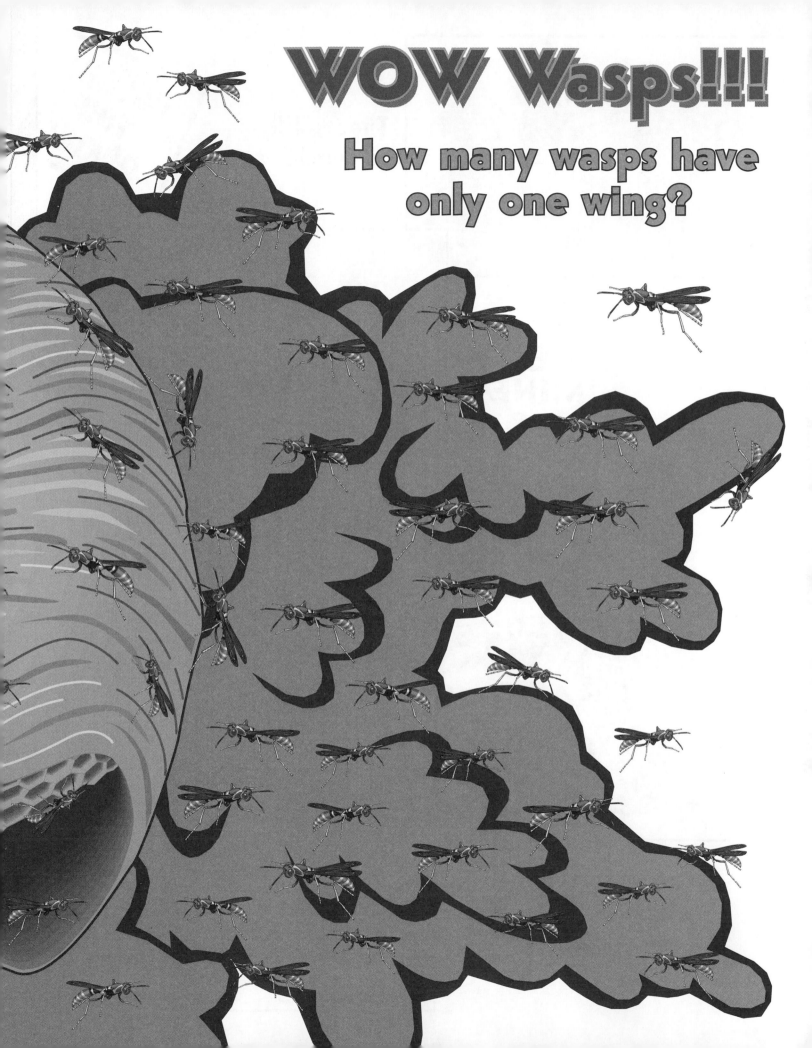

# WOW Wasps!!!

## How many wasps have only one wing?

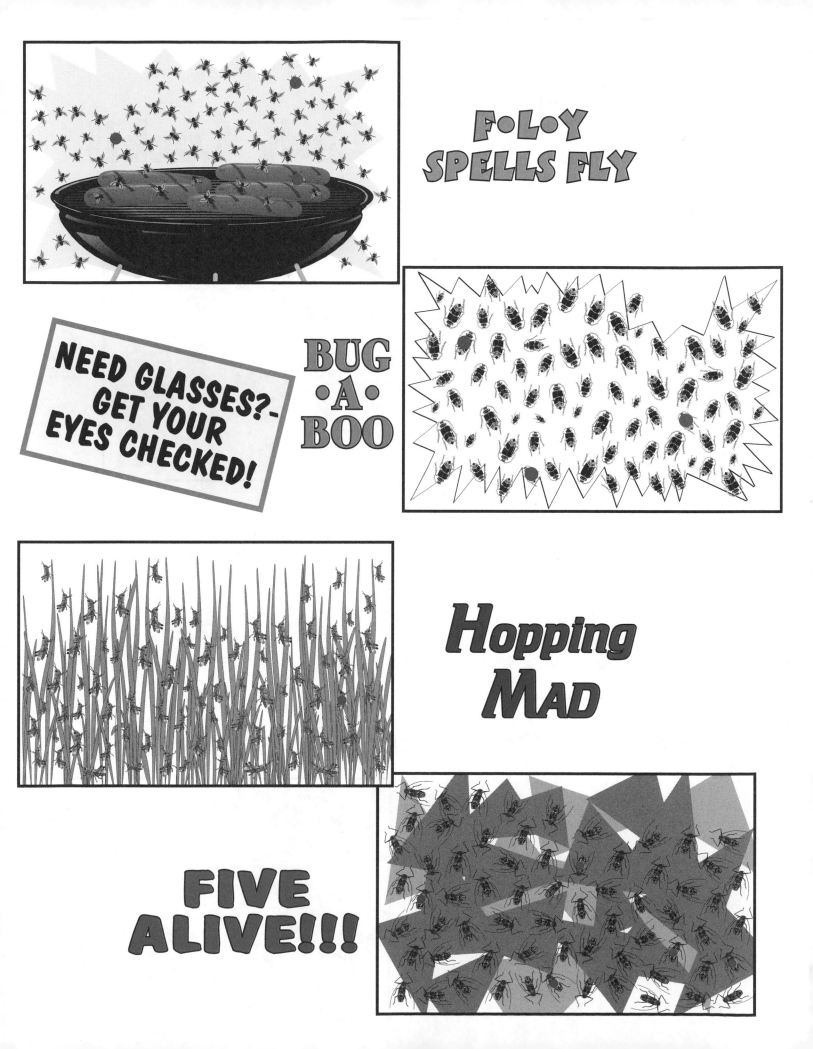

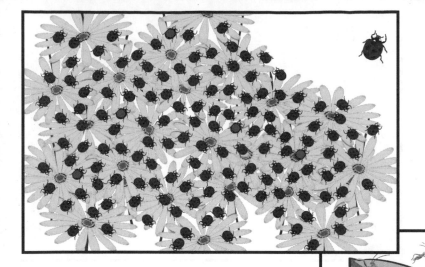

# Lady Luck!!

## Mantis Munch

# SPIDER SPASM

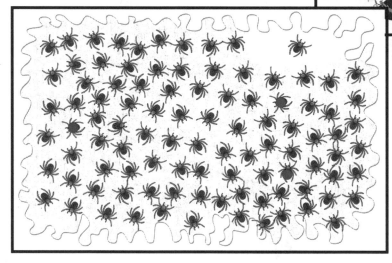

100 • 95 • (110) Sticks and Stones may. . .

# WOW Wasps!!!

**REST YOUR EYEBALLS!**

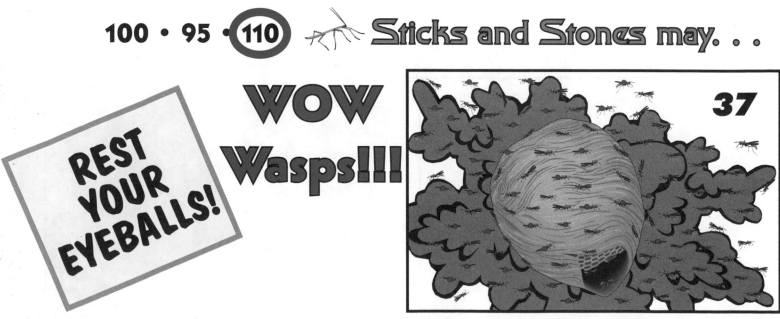